Why Math Puzzlers?

Research has shown that repetition is essential for the brain to learn and recall information. Furthermore, children have a tendency to repeat activities they enjoy. The engaging games and puzzles in this book will provide your child with repeated practice of grade-level-appropriate math skills. Continued practice with these skills helps develop a strong understanding of basic math concepts and builds a strong foundation in math problem solving, an important tool for academic success.

Upon your child's completion of each activity, use the provided incentive chart and stickers to track progress and celebrate your child's success.

SKILLS

- Numbers through 1,000
- Place value
- Addition
- Subtraction
- Money
- Time

- Geometry
- Fractions
- Pattern extension
- Word problems
- Logic
- Math vocabulary

HOW YOU CAN HELP SUPPORT LEARNING

- Have your child draw pictures or use equations with symbols to represent the data in addition and subtraction problems.
- Assist your child in identifying key math terms, such as *sum*, *difference*, *even*, *odd*, *equal*, *more than*, *greater than*, and *less than*.
- Ask your child to explain his or her answers.
- Give hints rather than solutions to particularly tricky problems.
- Have your child check answers to addition and subtraction problems by working backward.

Reprinted 2014
© 2012 Creative Teaching Press Inc., Huntington Beach, CA 92649
Reproduction of activities in any manner for use in the classroom and not for commercial sale is permissible.
Reproduction of these materials for an entire school or for a school system is strictly prohibited.

What's My Number?

Circle the correct answers.

1 I have 9 ones and less than 4 tens.
What number am I?

49   29

2 I have more than 6 tens and less than 5 ones.
What number am I?

91   33

3 I have less than 5 tens and more than 4 ones.
What number am I?

45   54

4 I have more than 3 ones and less than 7 tens.
What number am I?

88   56

5 I have less than 7 ones and more than 5 tens.
What number am I?

55   61

Math Riddle

Write the sums under the problems. To answer the riddle, find the letters that match the sums and write them on the lines below.

Match Box

20	17	19	14	13	16	9	12	18	15	11	10
B	S	V	I	P	E	M	H	O	R	A	L

Riddle

What did one math book say to the other math book?

8 + 6

7 + 5	5 + 6	11 + 8	8 + 8

8 + 5	7 + 8	9 + 9	10 +10	6 + 4	9 + 7	4 + 5	9 + 8

ANSWER:

___ ___ ___ ___ ___   ___ ___ ___ ___ ___ ___ ___ ___

Inching Along

Help the worm get to the watermelon. Make a path by circling the pictures that are measured in inches.

Abracadabra

Draw lines on the shapes below to make new shapes.

1 Draw 1 line to turn the rectangle into 2 triangles.

2 Draw 1 line to turn the rectangle into 2 squares.

3 Draw 2 lines to turn the square into 4 squares.

4 Draw 2 lines to turn the square into 4 triangles.

5 Draw 2 lines to turn the triangle into 3 triangles.

6 Draw 2 lines to turn the triangle into 3 triangles.
(Make your drawing different from 5)

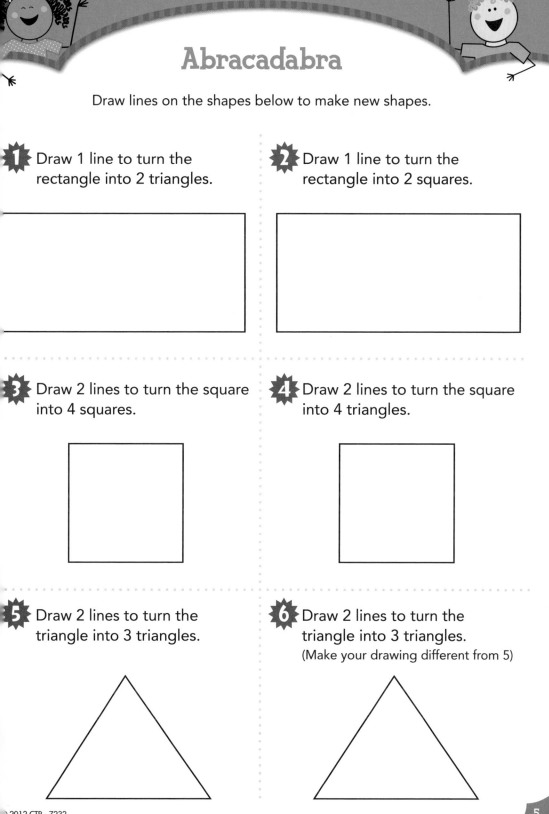

Bee Problems

Draw lines to match the subtraction problems to their differences.

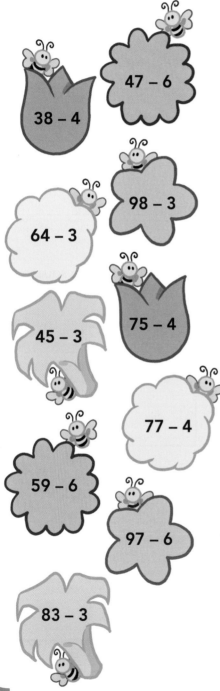

38 – 4

47 – 6

98 – 3

64 – 3

75 – 4

45 – 3

77 – 4

59 – 6

97 – 6

83 – 3

41

34

61

95

42

71

53

73

80

91

Hidden Facts

Circle the hidden addition and subtraction facts.
Add a **+** or **−** and an **=** for each fact.

1 (12 + 3 = 15)   1   16

2 26   22   12   10   20

3 7   3   10   7   70

4 11   32   6   26   30

5 3   25   5   20   15

6 44   9   36   45   20

7 14   3   11   6   10

8 21   15   8   23   16

Who's the Tallest

Read the clues. Then write each girl's name under the correct picture.

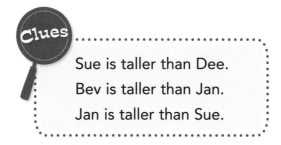

Clues

Sue is taller than Dee.
Bev is taller than Jan.
Jan is taller than Sue.

_____   _____   _____   _____

Go Figure!

Use the clues to fill in the grid with the correct numbers.

Across

2. #9 Down minus 602
4. Number of weeks in a year
5. #17 Down minus 53
7. #15 Down plus 15
8. Numbers 2678 in a different order
10. 45 doubled
12. 50 – 25
13. Numbers 2345 in a different order
15. 70 – 25
16. 8 + 5
17. 44 doubled
18. 79 + 66 + 77

Down

1. 64 – 32
2. 24 – 12
3. Numbers 0238 in a different order
4. #7 Across minus 10
6. 9 tens 2 ones
7. 500 + 105
9. 800 – 75
11. Numbers 1234 in a different order
14. 42 – 21
15. 39 + 9
17. 41 + 41
19. 100 – 80

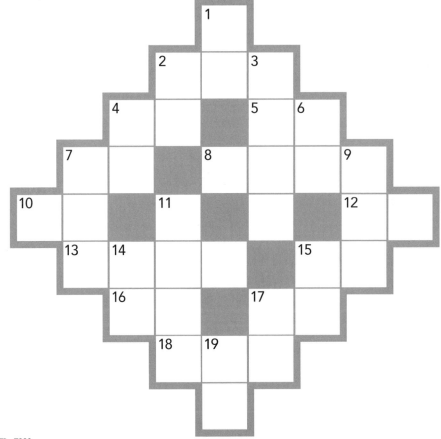

© 2012 CTP - 7232

9

Who's Who?

Read the clues. Then write each boy's name under the correct picture.

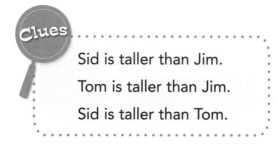

Clues

Sid is taller than Jim.

Tom is taller than Jim.

Sid is taller than Tom.

_____   _____   _____

Geometry Words

Find and circle the words from the Word Box.

ANGLE	CONE	CYLINDER	PYRAMID	PLANE
CUBE	PRISM	VERTEX	CORNER	FACE
SOLID	SPHERE	SYMMETRY	CONGRUENT	EDGE

```
C  Y  L  I  N  D  E  R  P  L  S  O  A  O
P  A  A  R  A  L  L  E  L  E  D  G  E  L
P  Y  R  A  M  I  D  E  A  G  A  B  C  I
A  S  C  O  N  E  R  O  N  P  O  P  O  E
R  O  Q  N  S  E  I  E  G  E  R  R  N  E
E  L  P  S  H  Y  U  D  L  Q  H  I  G  R
A  I  S  P  L  B  M  E  E  L  L  S  R  L
O  D  S  P  S  P  E  M  E  Q  A  M  U  L
H  E  T  P  E  M  L  L  E  Y  L  L  E  E
C  O  R  N  E  R  L  A  I  T  U  E  N  O
A  R  D  R  E  E  E  I  N  T  R  S  T  C
N  I  E  C  C  I  C  U  B  E  D  Y  S  N
G  P  E  A  V  E  R  T  E  X  T  E  R  U
G  L  F  L  Y  R  L  G  O  N  O  A  A  Q
```

Time Riddles

Fill in the blanks using these time words.

Word Box

year   hour   decade   day   week   minute

I am sixty seconds. I am a _____ .

I am sixty minutes. I am an _____ .

I am twenty-four hours. I am a _____ .

I am seven days. I am a _____ .

I am twelve months. I am a _____ .

I am ten years. I am a _____ .

Math Riddle

Write the sums under the problems. To answer the riddle, find the letters that match the sums and write them on the lines below.

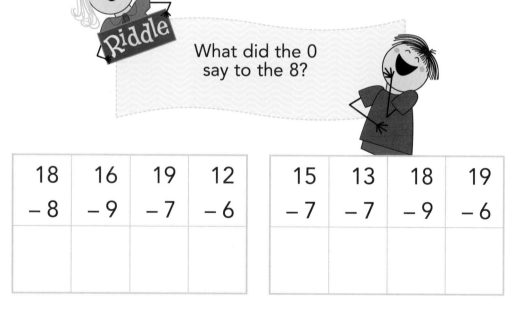

Match Box

6	10	12	13	9	7	8
E	N	C	T	L	I	B

Riddle

What did the 0 say to the 8?

18	16	19	12
− 8	− 9	− 7	− 6

15	13	18	19
− 7	− 7	− 9	− 6

ANSWER:

___ ___ ___ ___   ___ ___ ___ ___

Neighborhood Maze

Help Andy take three different paths home. Begin at each arrow and draw one path with a pencil. Then start with 19 and subtract the numbers along each path. Write your answers in the circles.

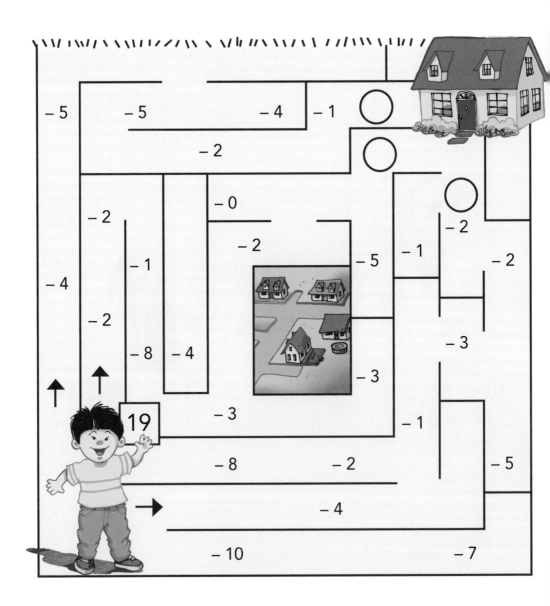

Tricky Squares

Count the total number of squares you see in each design.
Be careful. Some squares may be hidden.

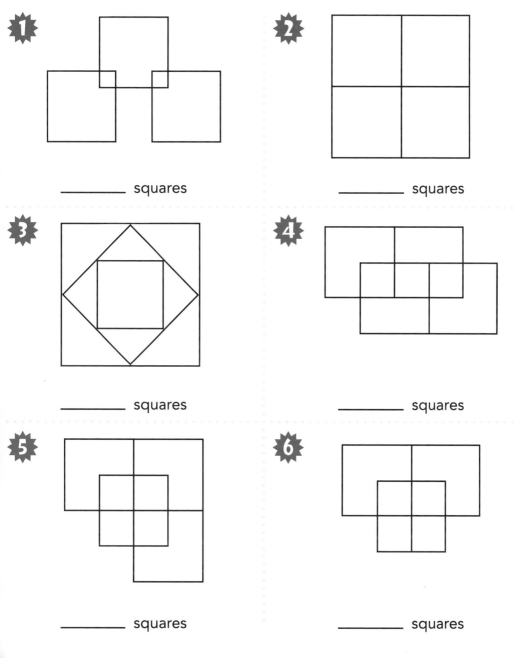

1 _____ squares

2 _____ squares

3 _____ squares

4 _____ squares

5 _____ squares

6 _____ squares

Volume and Weight Words

Find and circle the words from the Word Box.

Word Box

CUP	KILOGRAM	VOLUME	PINT	MILLILITER
QUART	POUND	CAPACITY	GRAM	GALLON
OUNCE	LITER	HEAVY	LIGHT	WEIGHT

```
P  P  Q  M  G  R  A  M  P  O  U  N  C  L
V  O  L  U  M  E  R  P  I  L  I  G  H  E
E  U  P  L  I  G  H  T  N  V  N  Q  Q  Y
C  N  L  I  T  E  R  D  A  M  R  U  U  P
A  T  I  L  I  D  N  E  A  L  L  A  A  W
P  U  K  M  C  U  H  R  P  I  N  T  R  E
A  L  G  I  O  U  G  O  G  I  M  M  T  I
C  E  I  P  L  O  U  U  H  A  R  L  V  G
I  T  G  G  L  O  N  G  E  L  C  O  H
T  V  T  I  H  M  G  C  T  A  A  L  Y  T
Y  A  K  Y  U  I  A  E  C  A  L  V  O  N
M  I  L  L  I  L  I  T  E  R  A  L  H  A
E  I  E  T  O  C  U  P  O  E  L  I  O  U
L  V  I  I  Y  M  V  A  H  H  A  L  I  N
```

Find the Facts

Circle the hidden addition and subtraction facts.
Add a **+** or **−** and an **=** for each fact.

1 (12 + 4 = 16) 18 10

2 7 2 8 10 80

3 9 2 18 2 16

4 5 6 10 16 30

5 3 15 9 6 13

6 24 9 33 45 20

7 17 4 13 6 10

8 21 15 28 13 15

That's Some Clown!

Read the clues. Then write the correct name below each clown.

Clues

One clown has juggled for 8 years, one has juggled for 11 years, and one has juggled for 16 years.

Chuckles has juggled 8 years more than clown A.

One clown is named Scooter.

Clown B has juggled 3 years longer than Bobo.

A   B   C

_____   _____   _____

Go Figure!

Use the clues to fill in the grid with the correct numbers.

Across

2. 150 + 82
4. 38 + 36
5. One dozen
7. 22 rounded to the nearest ten
8. Numbers 2645 in a different order
10. Number of months in three years
12. Number of hours in two days
13. Two thousand one hundred eighteen
15. 17 + 11
16. 74 − 32
17. 17 + 72
18. 220 − 110

Down

1. 54 + 9
2. Number of hours in a day
3. Numbers 2061 in a different order
4. 65 rounded to the nearest ten
6. Two dozen plus one
7. 280 − 18
9. 200 + 40 + 8
11. Numbers 1128 in a different order
14. #6 Down minus 11
15. 2 tens 9 ones
17. 79 rounded to the nearest ten
19. #18 Across minus 100

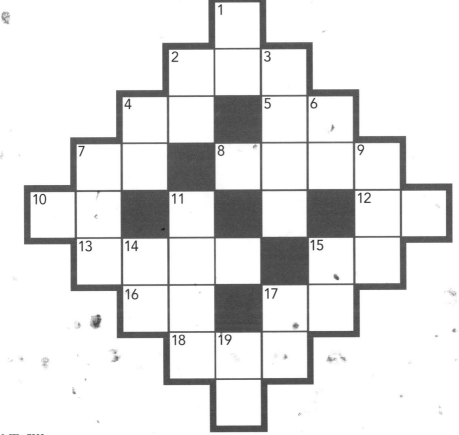

Here, Kitty-Kitty!

Read the clues. Then write each cat's name under the correct picture.

Clues

The cat called Fluffy has a striped tail.

Ginger is next to cat B.

Lucky is next to the cat that's lying down.

A   B   C

_____   _____   _____

Does This Measure Up?

Find and circle the words from the Word Box.

WIDTH	NEAR	METER	KILOMETER	INCH
HEIGHT	FOOT	MILE	DISTANCE	FAR
PERIMETER	YARD	LENGTH	CENTIMETER	AREA

```
T  N  E  A  R  L  K  H  R  C  F  O  O  T
D  E  P  T  A  K  C  E  N  T  I  M  E  E
D  I  S  T  A  N  I  E  T  F  A  R  E  E
D  W  C  K  I  P  R  L  M  I  R  T  E  Y
I  I  E  W  I  D  T  I  O  R  E  D  R  M
S  D  N  H  W  H  A  M  E  M  A  M  R  C
T  T  T  H  I  M  I  L  E  E  E  E  A  I
A  H  I  E  D  Y  M  E  T  H  T  T  L  I
N  I  M  I  T  T  A  I  G  E  H  N  E  D
C  I  E  G  M  H  M  R  M  H  E  O  L  R
E  M  T  H  L  E  E  R  D  L  I  E  M  T
L  W  E  T  L  E  N  G  T  H  G  S  O  W
K  I  R  O  P  E  R  I  M  E  T  E  R  T
R  H  K  T  C  A  A  O  K  H  T  F  T  L
```

Snaky Patterns

Fill in the missing numbers.

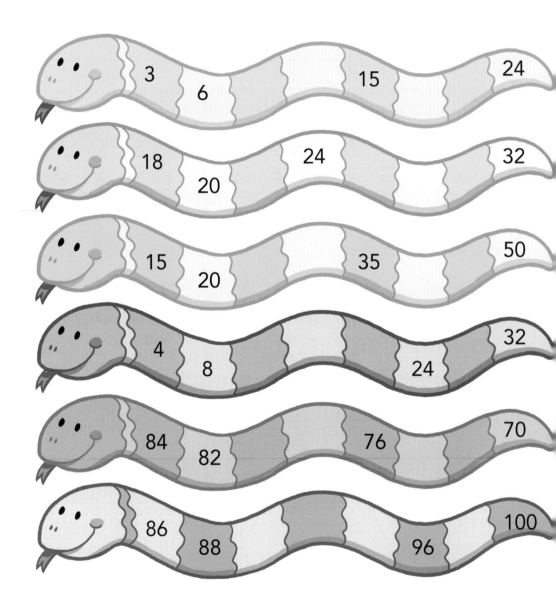

Math Riddle

Write the sums under the problems. To answer the riddle, find
the letters that match the sums and write them on the lines below.

Match Box

19	16	20	22	17	21	18	15
S	A	Y	T	E	L	D	R

Riddle

Where can you buy a
ruler that is three feet long?

8 + 8	11 + 11

9 + 7

10 + 10	6 + 10	7 + 8	9 + 9

10 + 9	11 + 5	10 + 11	8 + 9

ANSWER:

___ ___   ___   ___ ___   ___ ___ ___ ___

2012 CTP - 7232

23

Outer Space Sums

Add each problem on the path to help the alien get to his planet.

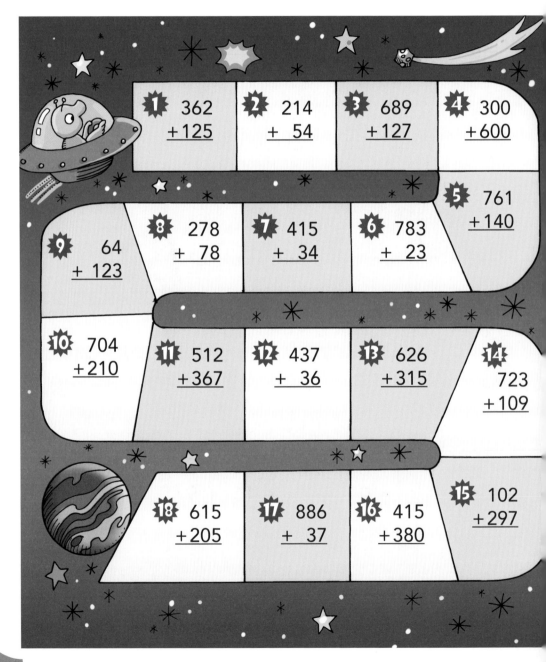

1 362 +125

2 214 + 54

3 689 +127

4 300 +600

5 761 +140

6 783 + 23

7 415 + 34

8 278 + 78

9 64 + 123

10 704 +210

11 512 +367

12 437 + 36

13 626 +315

14 723 +109

15 102 +297

16 415 +380

17 886 + 37

18 615 +205

Tricky Triangles

Count the total number of triangles you see in each design.
Be careful. Some triangles may be hidden!

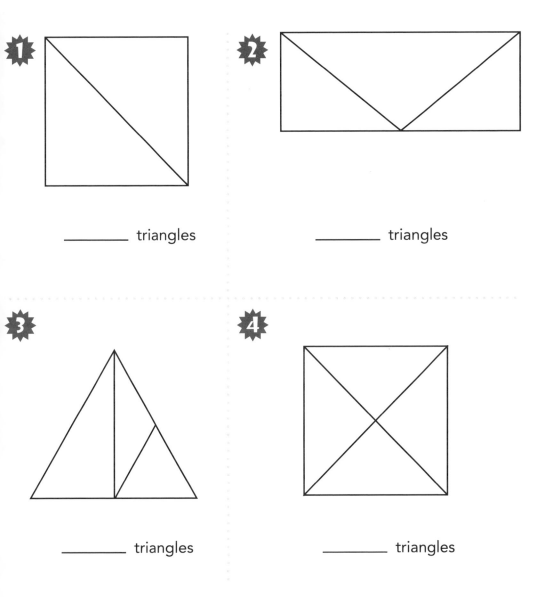

1

_____ triangles

2

_____ triangles

3

_____ triangles

4

_____ triangles

Racing to Get in Order

Write flag numbers in order from least to greatest.

1  235 532 325

_____, _____, _____

2  419 194 491

_____, _____, _____

3  763 736 673

_____, _____, _____

4  905 590 950

_____, _____, _____

Spot the Facts

Circle the hidden addition and subtraction facts.
Add a **+** or **−** and an **=** for each fact.

1   3   5   (2 + 8 = 10)

2   12   3   15   1   5

3   4   8   6   2   3

4   6   4   10   40   10

5   20   50   20   30   40

6   11   9   13   6   7

7   24   22   10   40   50

8   18   5   13   10   4

Four numbers are missing from the box. When all 15 numbers are together and in order, they increase by 7 and are between 0 and 100. Write the missing numbers.

43   71   ?   8

85   50

29   ?   1   ?

78   22

99   ?   57

The missing numbers are: _____ _____ _____ _____

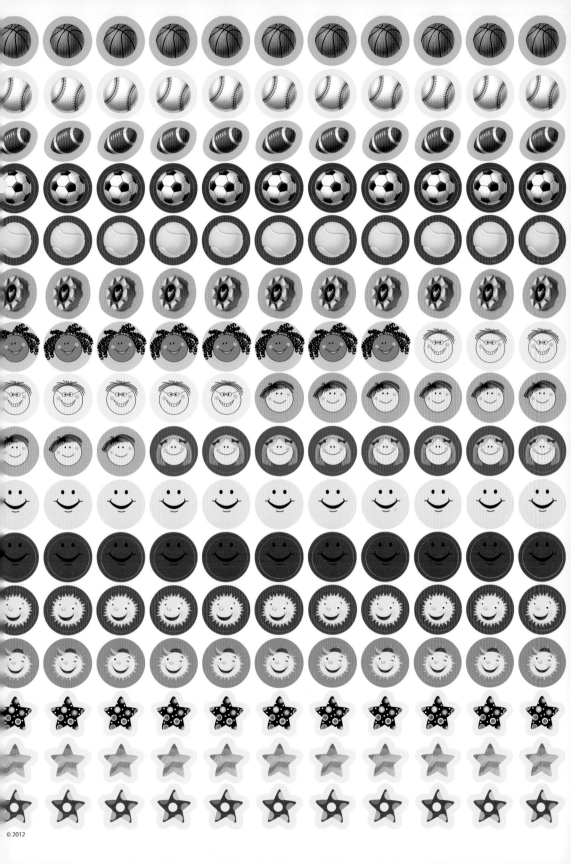

© 2012

Go Figure!

Use the clues to fill in the grid with the correct numbers.

Across

2. Number of hours in a day plus 100
4. 35 – 7
5. 7 doubled
7. Number of minutes in an hour
8. Numbers 4036 in a different order
10. Number of hours in a day
12. 54 – 7
13. Numbers 5432 in a different order
15. Three dozen
16. #5 Across plus seven
17. 100 – 15
18. #2 Across plus 106

Down

1. One dozen
2. #4 Across minus 10
3. Numbers 0134 in a different order
4. 15 rounded to the nearest ten
6. Ten less than fifty
7. #2 Across plus 518
9. 500 – 54
11. Numbers 1234 in a different order
14. #15 Across minus four
15. #17 Across minus 50
17. #7 Across plus 20
19. #15 Down plus three

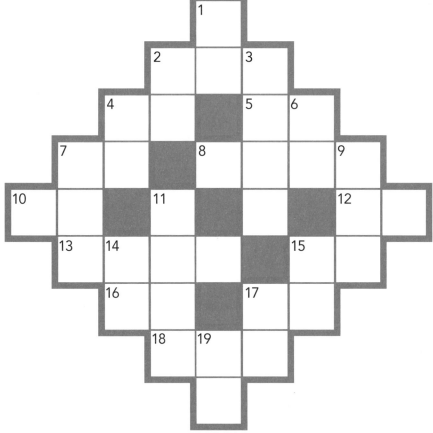

Mystery Numbers

Read the clues and use the set of numbers to write each mystery number.

1 The number is even. It is greater than 35. It is less than 50.

5 2 6 3

_____

2 The number is odd. It is greater than 85. It is less than 90.

9 8 2 5

_____

3 The number is even. It is greater than 60. It is less than 70.

3 7 6 2

_____

4 The number is odd. It is greater than 45. It is less than 75.

3 9 4 2

_____

5 The number is even. It is greater than 25. It is less than 30.

2 8 4 3

_____

6 The number is odd. It is greater than 80. It is less than 95.

1 9 7 4

_____

Search for Time and Place

Find and circle the words from the Word Box.

FRONT	NEXT	BESIDE	BEFORE	AFTER
BETWEEN	FIRST	BELOW	BACK	ABOVE
EARLY	LAST	MIDDLE	PAST	LATE

```
B  E  T  B  B  E  L  E  A  R  L  E  A  L
E  T  B  E  A  L  Y  B  L  A  I  B  B  R
T  O  E  M  W  C  L  R  D  B  A  B  O  E
W  F  I  I  L  L  K  A  A  O  F  E  V  B
E  E  T  D  P  A  S  T  I  E  T  T  E  E
E  E  A  D  B  E  S  I  D  E  E  W  F  T
L  T  I  L  F  R  O  N  T  T  R  E  W  R
I  M  B  E  F  R  L  B  N  E  R  E  E  L
B  E  F  O  R  E  T  A  E  I  A  N  K  B
T  L  A  T  E  R  R  D  F  L  L  R  E  E
S  B  E  S  I  F  L  A  T  L  O  A  L  F
S  D  Y  F  E  O  B  N  E  X  T  W  S  Y
B  E  F  O  E  F  I  R  S  T  E  E  L  T
B  T  E  E  E  E  B  I  F  A  V  O  W  E
```

High in the Sky

Write the missing numbers.

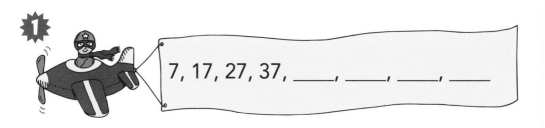

1 7, 17, 27, 37, _____, _____, _____, _____

2 30, 28, 26, 24, _____, _____, _____, _____

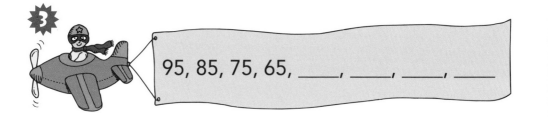

3 95, 85, 75, 65, _____, _____, _____, _____

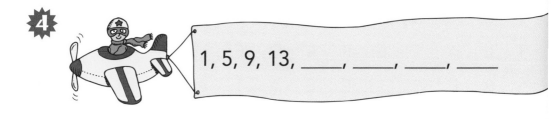

4 1, 5, 9, 13, _____, _____, _____, _____

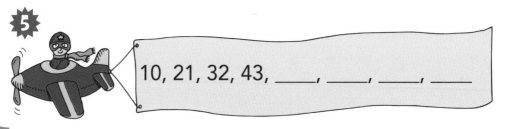

5 10, 21, 32, 43, _____, _____, _____, _____

Math Riddle

Write the differences under the problems. To answer the riddle, find the letters that match the differences and write them on the lines below.

14	11	8	6	7	15	9	10
N	E	S	G	V	I	T	H

Riddle

Why is six afraid of seven?
Because...

15	17	16	15	18
− 7	− 6	− 9	− 4	− 4

18	18	15	20	17
− 7	− 3	− 9	− 10	− 8

18	19	20	19
− 4	− 4	− 6	− 8

ANSWER:

___ ___ ___ ___ ___   ___ ___ ___ ___

Hidden Sums of 50

Find three numbers in a row **across**, **down**, or on a **diagonal** that add up to the sum of 50. Circle each set of three numbers.

22	16	36	23	21	16	30
5	15	21	16	15	29	10
10	14	13	19	23	25	10
15	5	36	17	31	35	25
26	35	18	19	18	17	33
19	10	5	26	19	15	17
32	4	5	14	15	17	9
22	9	19	25	24	14	16
19	6	29	11	3	28	15

I found _____ sums of 50.

More Tricky Triangles

Count the total number of triangles you see in each design.
Be careful. Some triangles may be hidden!

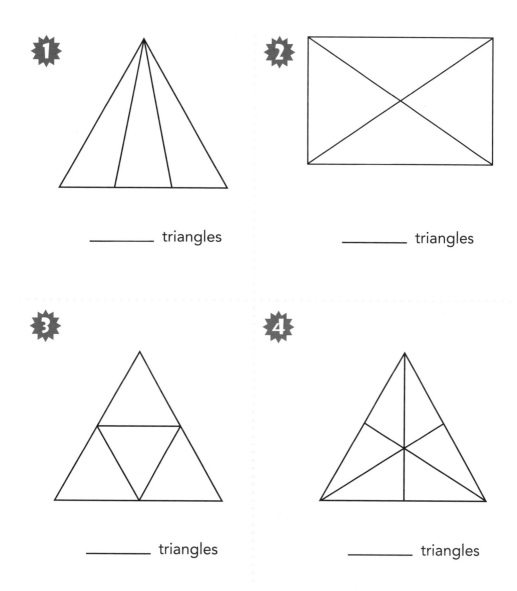

1

_____ triangles

2

_____ triangles

3

_____ triangles

4

_____ triangles

Fractured Fractions

Draw lines on the shapes below. Then shade them.

1 Divide the rectangle into thirds. Then shade $\frac{2}{3}$.

2 Divide the circle into half. Then shade $\frac{1}{2}$.

3 Divide the circle into fourths. Then shade $\frac{3}{4}$.

4 Divide the hexagon into sixths. Then shade $\frac{3}{6}$.

5 Divide the rectangle into eighths. Then shade $\frac{7}{8}$.

6 Divide the square into fourths. Then shade $\frac{1}{4}$.

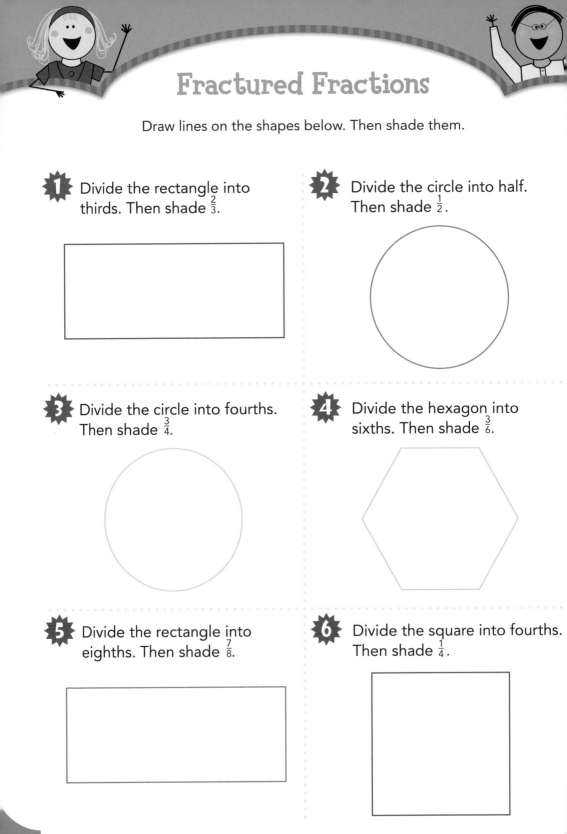

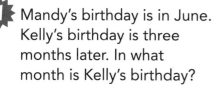

What Month Is It?

Write the month that answers the question.

1 Mandy's birthday is in June. Kelly's birthday is three months later. In what month is Kelly's birthday?

_____

2 Brian's birthday is five months before Jordan's birthday. Jordan's birthday is in August. In what month is Brian's birthday?

_____

3 Mrs. Garcia's son turned eight months old in October. In what month was he born?

_____

4 Joel visited his uncle for two months. He returned home at the beginning of September. In what month did he arrive at his uncle's house?

_____

Months of the Year
January
February
March
April
May
June
July
August
September
October
November
December

Missing Numbers

Four numbers are missing from the box. When all 13 numbers are together and in order, they increase by 8 and are between 0 and 100. Write the missing numbers.

73   25   ?

?   1   9

49   97

81   ?

57   ?   41

The missing numbers are: _____ _____ _____ _____

Go Figure!

Use the clues to fill in the grid with the correct numbers.

Across

2. 99 + 35
4. 4 + 4 + 4 + 4
5. 23 + 15
7. 90 – 9
8. Numbers 2143 in a different order
10. Number of hours in a day
12. 20 + 5
13. Numbers 6810 in a different order
15. 85 + 6
16. 22 doubled
17. #16 Across plus two
18. #1 Down plus 101

Down

1. 70 – 7
2. 1 ten 6 ones
3. Numbers 2346 in a different order
4. One more than 10
6. #14 Down minus one
7. 900 – 59
9. 400 + 20 + 1
11. Numbers 1346 in a different order
14. 100 – 16
15. #15 Across plus five
17. 4 tens 4 ones
19. #1 Down plus two

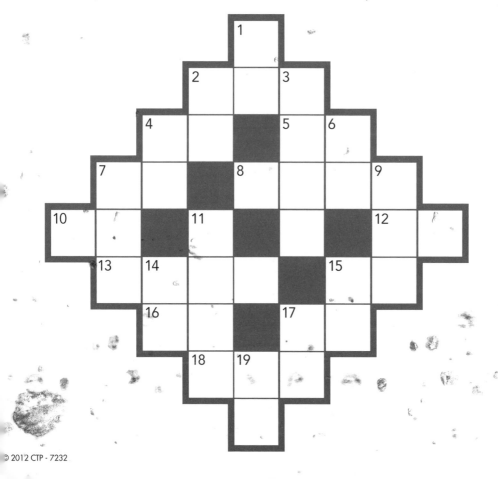

What's My Number?

Circle the correct number.

1 I have three hundreds. I have 2 ones and more than 6 tens.
What number am I?

372 352

2 I have seven hundreds. I have 8 tens and more than 7 ones.
What number am I?

789 786

3 I have five hundreds. I have 4 tens and less than 5 ones.
What number am I?

547 543

4 I have nine hundreds. I have less than 7 ones and more than 5 tens.
What number am I?

955 961

Search for Number Concepts

Find and circle the words from the Word Box.

WHOLE	SUM	ORDINAL	PRODUCT	MULTIPLY
ESTIMATE	ADD	ADDEND	EQUAL	SUBTRACT
REGROUP	HALF	FRACTION	DIFFERENCE	DIGITS

```
C  A  D  D  E  N  D  L  L  L  D  Y  E  C
C  W  H  O  L  E  R  U  A  E  L  D  G  R
A  F  N  A  U  T  A  N  T  P  T  I  R  P
R  R  E  A  G  Q  I  A  I  C  T  F  E  L
D  A  Q  T  Q  D  M  T  A  D  A  F  G  A
I  C  U  E  R  I  L  R  L  A  D  E  R  T
N  T  A  O  T  U  T  L  S  L  T  R  O  L
I  I  L  S  M  B  O  U  D  O  M  E  U  T
Y  O  E  O  U  H  A  L  F  U  S  N  P  M
O  N  L  S  W  T  O  M  S  F  R  C  I  D
E  Q  U  A  U  F  R  A  C  T  C  E  M  U
U  A  D  D  I  S  D  I  G  I  T  S  O  C
H  E  L  F  L  I  P  R  O  D  U  C  T  R
L  O  R  A  H  C  T  C  R  L  G  Q  A  P
```

The Shape of Things to Come

Draw shapes in the boxes to continue each pattern.

1

2

3

4

5

Math Riddle

Write the differences under the problems. To answer the riddle, find the letters that match the differences and write them on the lines below.

Match Box

10	8	4	7	6	5	11	12	9
S	O	C	H	A	T	I	M	E

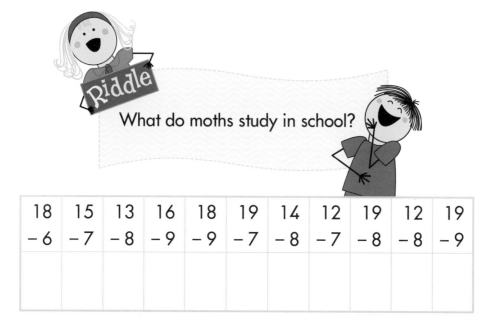

Riddle

What do moths study in school?

18	15	13	16	18	19	14	12	19	12	19
− 6	− 7	− 8	− 9	− 9	− 7	− 8	− 7	− 8	− 8	− 9

ANSWER:

___ ___ ___ ___ ___ ___ ___ ___ ___ ___ ___

43

Ant's Path to 0

Help the ant find the food. Begin at the number under **"Start."** Draw the path of numbers that when subtracted equals 0. End at the number above **"End."**

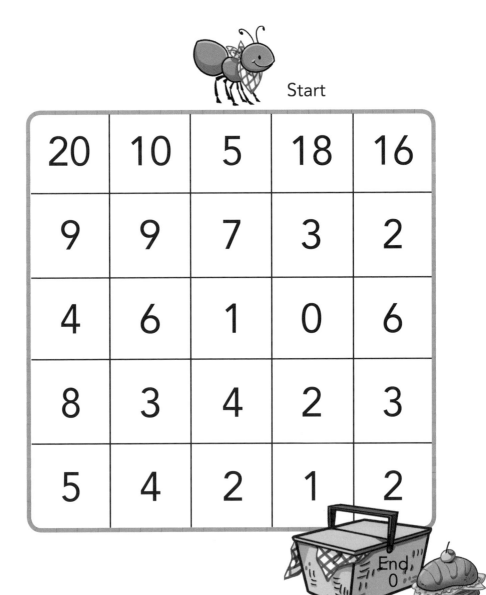

Start

20	10	5	18	16
9	9	7	3	2
4	6	1	0	6
8	3	4	2	3
5	4	2	1	2

End
0

Groups of the Same

Draw a picture to help you write an equation and solve each problem.

1 5 pigs in a litter;
2 litters in the pen.
Put them together,
and you will get _____.

_____ + _____ = _____

2 3 grapes in a bunch;
3 bunches on the vine.
Put them together,
and you will get _____.

____ + ____ + ____ = ____

3 2 dogs in a pack;
3 packs fetching sticks.
Put them together,
and you will get _____.

____ + ____ + ____ = ____

4 4 horses in a team;
2 teams by the gate.
Put them together,
and you will get _____.

___ + ___ = ____

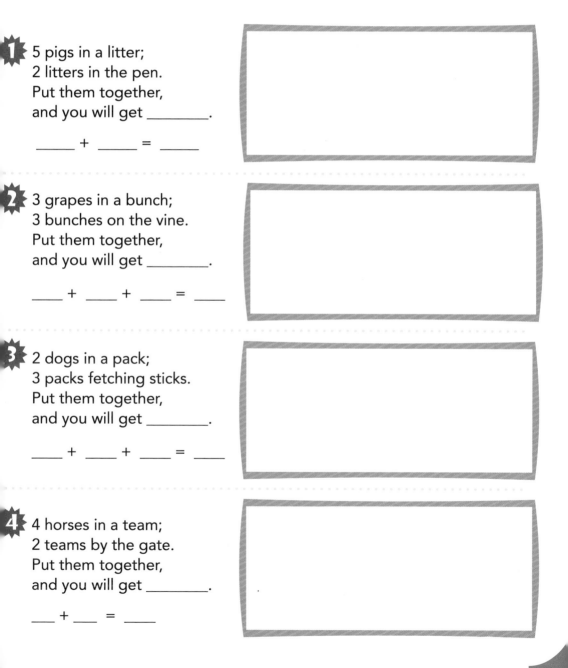

Matching Faces

Look at the shaded face of each solid.
Color the shape that matches the face.

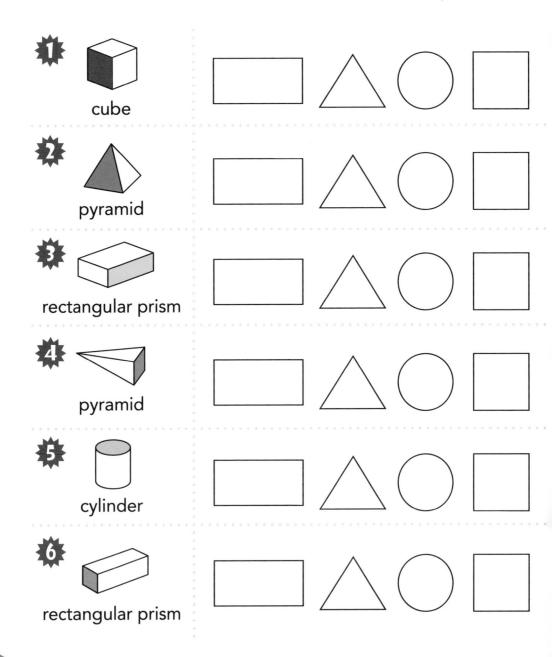

1. cube

2. pyramid

3. rectangular prism

4. pyramid

5. cylinder

6. rectangular prism

Do You Recognize My Face?

Write the name of the solid shape that matches each clue.

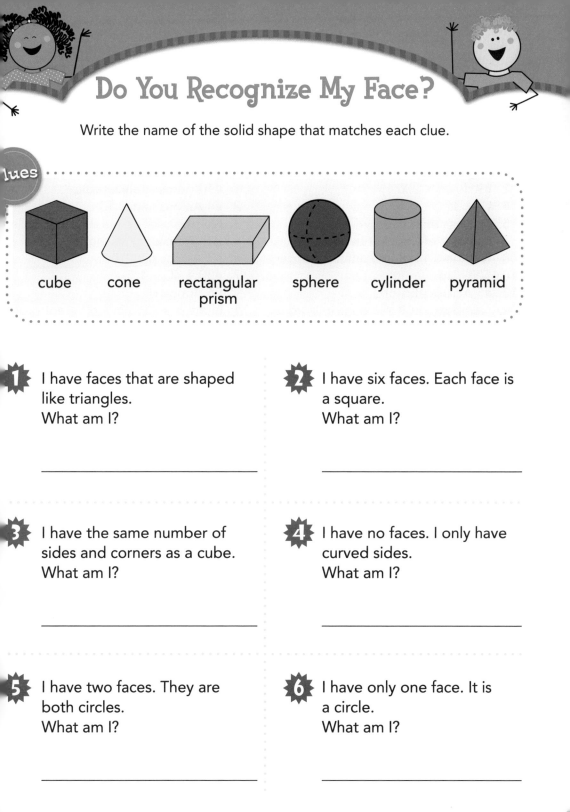

cube   cone   rectangular prism   sphere   cylinder   pyramid

1 I have faces that are shaped like triangles.
What am I?

_____

2 I have six faces. Each face is a square.
What am I?

_____

3 I have the same number of sides and corners as a cube.
What am I?

_____

4 I have no faces. I only have curved sides.
What am I?

_____

5 I have two faces. They are both circles.
What am I?

_____

6 I have only one face. It is a circle.
What am I?

_____

Go Figure!

Use the clues to fill in the grid with the correct numbers.

Across

- **2.** #9 down + 200
- **4.** 42 + 34
- **5.** Ten less than twenty-five
- **7.** Number of hours in two days
- **8.** Numbers 1478 in a different order
- **10.** 100 – 16
- **12.** #5 Across plus one
- **13.** Numbers 2468 in a different order
- **15.** Number of weeks in a year
- **16.** #15 Down plus seven
- **17.** 43 doubled
- **18.** 200 + 15

Down

- **1.** #10 Across minus three
- **2.** #4 Across minus 40
- **3.** Numbers 1234 in a different order
- **4.** #17 Across minus eight
- **6.** #7 Across plus 10
- **7.** 400 + 40 + 4
- **9.** 56 doubled
- **11.** Numbers 2358 in a different order
- **14.** #7 Across minus 22
- **15.** #4 Across minus 20
- **17.** 76 + 9
- **19.** 15 + 4

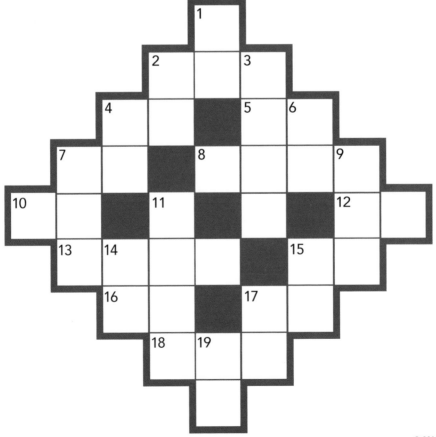

Missing Numbers

Four numbers are missing from the box. When all 12 numbers are together and in order, they increase by 9 and are between 0 and 101. Write the missing numbers.

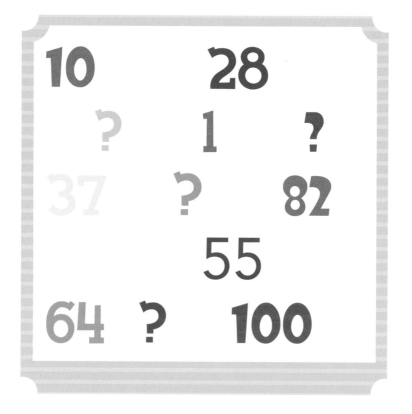

10   28

   ?   1   ?

37   ?   82

      55

64   ?   100

The missing numbers are: _____ _____ _____ _____

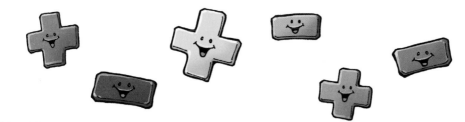

Name That Hen!

Read the clues. Then write the correct name below each hen.

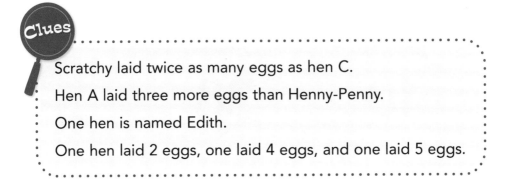

Clues

Scratchy laid twice as many eggs as hen C.

Hen A laid three more eggs than Henny-Penny.

One hen is named Edith.

One hen laid 2 eggs, one laid 4 eggs, and one laid 5 eggs.

A   B   C

_____   _____   _____

What's the Magic Rule?

Subtract to find the magic rule that changes the **IN** numbers to the **OUT** numbers. Then fill in the missing numbers and write the rule at the bottom of each box.

1

IN	OUT
18	15
12	9
10	
16	
20	
15	

RULE: – 3

2

IN	OUT
15	10
16	11
17	
18	
19	
10	

RULE:

3

IN	OUT
5	1
12	8
8	
10	
14	
20	

RULE:

4

IN	OUT
12	6
10	4
16	
14	
11	
18	

RULE:

Answer Key

PAGE 2

What's My Number?

Circle the correct answers.

1. I have 9 ones and less than 4 tens.
   What number am I?
   49   (29)

2. I have more than 6 tens and less than 5 ones.
   What number am I?
   (91)   33

3. I have less than 5 tens and more than 4 ones.
   What number am I?
   (45)   54

4. I have more than 3 ones and less than 7 tens.
   What number am I?
   88   (56)

5. I have less than 7 ones and more than 5 tens.
   What number am I?
   55   (61)

PAGE 3

Math Riddle

Write the sums under the problems. To answer the riddle, find the letters that match the sums and write them on the lines below.

Match Box
20	17	14	13	16	9	12	18	15	11	10
B	S	V	I	P	E	M	H	O	R	A	L

What did one math book say to the other math book?

8 + 6		7 + 5	5 + 6	11 + 8	8 + 8
14		12	11	19	16

8 + 5	7 + 8	9 + 9	10 + 10	6 + 4	9 + 7	4 + 5	9 + 8
13	15	18	20	10	16	9	17

ANSWER
I HAVE PROBLEMS

PAGE 4

Inching Along

Help the worm get to the watermelon. Make a path by circling the pictures that are measured in inches.

PAGE 5
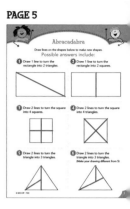

Abracadabra

Draw lines on the shapes below to make new shapes.
Possible answers include:

1. Draw 1 line to turn the rectangle into 2 triangles.

2. Draw 1 line to turn the rectangle into 2 squares.

3. Draw 2 lines to turn the square into 4 squares.

4. Draw 2 lines to turn the square into 4 triangles.

5. Draw 2 lines to turn the triangle into 3 triangles.

6. Draw 2 lines to turn the triangle into 3 triangles. (Make your drawing different from 5)

PAGE 6

Bee Problems

Draw lines to match the subtraction problems to their differences.

PAGE 7

Hidden Facts

Circle the hidden addition and subtraction facts. Add a + or − and an = for each fact.

1. 12 + 3 = 15   1   16
2. 26   (22 − 12 = 10)   20
3. (7 + 3 = 10)   7   70
4. 11   (32 − 6 = 26)   30
5. 3   (25 − 5 = 20)   15
6. 44   (9 + 36 = 45)   20
7. (14 − 3 = 11)   6   10
8. 21   (15 + 8 = 23)   16

PAGE 8

Who's the Tallest

Read the clues. Then write each girl's name under the correct picture.

Clues
Sue is taller than Dee.
Bev is taller than Jan.
Jan is taller than Sue.

Dee   Sue   Jan   Bev

PAGE 9

Go Figure!

Use the clues to fill in the grid with the correct numbers.

Across
2. #9 Down minus 602
4. Number of weeks in a year
5. #17 Down minus 53
7. #15 Down plus 15
8. Numbers 2678 in a different order
10. 45 doubled
12. 50 − 25
13. Numbers 2345 in a different order
15. 70 − 25
16. 8 + 5
17. 44 doubled
18. 79 + 66 + 77

Down
1. 64 − 32
2. 24 − 12
3. Numbers 0238 in a different order
6. #7 Across minus 10
9. 9 tens 2 ones
7. 500 + 105
9. 800 − 75
11. Numbers 1234 in a different order
14. 42 − 21
15. 39 + 9
17. 41 + 41
19. 100 − 80

PAGE 10

Who's Who?

Read the clues. Then write each boy's name under the correct picture.

Clues
Sid is taller than Jim.
Tom is taller than Jim.
Sid is taller than Tom.

Jim   Tom   Sid

PAGE 11

Geometry Words

Find and circle the words from the Word Box.

Word Box
ANGLE   CONE   CYLINDER   PYRAMID   PLANE
CUBE   PRISM   VERTEX   CORNER   FACE
SOLID   SPHERE   SYMMETRY   CONGRUENT   EDGE

```
C Y L I N D E R P L S O A O
P A A R A L L E L E D G E L
P Y R A M I D E A G A B C P
A S C O N E R D N P O P O E
R O Q N G S C E G E R R N E
E L P S H U D L Q H I G R F
L B P L B M F E L L S R L
O D G P S P E M E Q A M U L
H E T P E M L E Y L L E
C O R N E R L A T N E O
A R D R E B E I N R S T C
N I E C C C U B E D Y S N
G P E A V E R T E X T E R U
G L F Y R L G O N O A A Q
```

PAGE 12

Time Riddles

Fill in the blanks using these time words.

Word Box
year   hour   decade   day   week   minute

I am sixty seconds. I am a __minute__

I am sixty minutes. I am an __hour__

I am twenty-four hours. I am a __day__

I am seven days. I am a __week__

I am twelve months. I am a __year__

I am ten years. I am a __decade__

PAGE 13

Math Riddle

Write the sums under the problems. To answer the riddle, find the letters that match the sums and write them on the lines below.

Match Box
6	10	12	13	9	7	8
E	N	C	T	L	I	B

What did the 0 say to the 8?

18 − 8	16 − 9	19 − 7		15 − 7	13 − 7	18 − 9	19 − 6
10	7	12	6	8	6	9	13

NICE BELT

PAGE 14

Neighborhood Maze

Help Andy take three different paths home. Begin at each arrow and draw one path with a pencil. Then start with 19 and add or subtract the numbers along each path. Write your answers in the circles.

PAGE 15

Tricky Squares

Count the total number of squares you see in each design. Be careful. Some squares may be hidden.

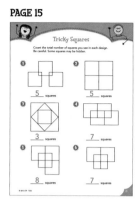

① 5 squares
② 5 squares
③ 3 squares
④ 7 squares
⑤ 8 squares
⑥ 7 squares

PAGE 16

Volume and Weight Words

Find and circle the words from the Word Box.

Word Box: CUP, KILOGRAM, VOLUME, PINT, MILLILITER, QUART, POUND, CAPACITY, GRAM, GALLON, OUNCE, LITER, HEAVY, LIGHT, WEIGHT

PAGE 17

Find the Facts

Circle the hidden addition and subtraction facts. Add a + or − and an = for each fact.

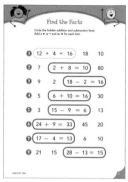

① 12 + 4 = 16   18   10
② 7   2 + 8 = 10   80
③ 9   2   18 − 2 = 16
④ 5   6 + 10 = 16   30
⑤ 3   15 − 9 = 6   13
⑥ 24 + 9 = 33   45   20
⑦ 17 − 4 = 13   6   10
⑧ 21   15   28 − 13 = 15

PAGE 18

That's Some Clown!

Read the clues. Then write the correct name below each clown.

One clown has juggled for 8 years, one has juggled for 11 years, and one has juggled for 16 years.
Chuckles has juggled 8 years more than clown A.
One clown is named Scooter.
Clown B has juggled 3 years longer than Bobo.

A. Bobo   B. Scooter   C. Chuckles

PAGE 19

Go Figure!

Use the clues to fill in the grid with the correct numbers.

Across
2. 150 + 82
4. 38 + 36
5. One dozen
7. 22 rounded to the nearest ten
8. Numbers 2645 in a different order
10. Number of months in three years
13. Two thousand one hundred eighteen
15. 17 + 11
16. 74 − 32
17. 47 + 72
18. 220 − 110

Down
1. 54 + 9
2. Number of hours in a day
3. Numbers 2061 in a different order
4. 45 rounded to the nearest ten
6. Two dozen plus one
7. 280 − 18
9. 200 + 40 + 8
11. Numbers 1128 in a different order
12. 46 Down minus 11
14. 2 tens 9 ones
17. 79 rounded to the nearest ten
19. #18 Across minus 100

PAGE 20

Here, Kitty-Kitty!

Read the clues. Then write each cat's name under the correct picture.

The cat called Fluffy has a striped tail.
Ginger is next to cat B.
Lucky is next to the cat that's lying down.

A. Fluffy   B. Lucky   C. Ginger

PAGE 21

Does This Measure Up?

Find and circle the words from the Word Box.

WIDTH, NEAR, METER, KILOMETER, INCH, HEIGHT, FOOT, MILE, DISTANCE, FAR, PERIMETER, YARD, LENGTH, CENTIMETER, AREA

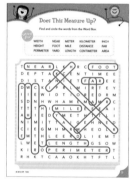

PAGE 22

Snaky Patterns

Fill in the missing numbers.

PAGE 23

Math Riddle

Write the sums under the problems. To answer the riddle, find the letters that match the sums and write them on the lines below.

19	16	20	22	17	21	18	15
S	A	Y	T	E	L	D	R

Where can you buy a ruler that is three feet long?

9 + 8 + 11 = 16   6 + 7 = 22   10 + 10 + 8 = 16   2 + 9 = 16 15 18
16   22   20

10 11 10   8
+ 9 + 5 + 11 + 17
19 16   21 17

ANSWER:
AT A YARD SALE

PAGE 24

Outer Space Sums

Add each problem on the path to help the alien get to his planet.

PAGE 25

Tricky Triangles

Count the total number of triangles you see in each design. Be careful. Some triangles may be hidden!

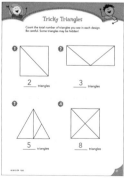

① 2 triangles
② 3 triangles
③ 5 triangles
④ 8 triangles

PAGE 26
Racing to Get in Order

Write flag numbers in order from least to greatest.

1. 235 532 325 → 235 325 532
2. 419 194 491 → 194 419 491
3. 763 736 673 → 673 736 763
4. 905 590 950 → 590 905 950

PAGE 27
Spot the Facts

Circle the hidden addition and subtraction facts. Add a + or − and an = for each fact.

1. 3 5 (2 + 8 = 10)
2. (12 + 3 = 15) 1 5
3. 4 (8 − 6 = 2) 3
4. (6 + 4 = 10) 40 10
5. 20 (50 − 20 = 30) 40
6. 11 9 (13 − 6 = 7)
7. 24 22 (10 + 40 = 50)
8. (18 − 5 = 13) 10 4

PAGE 28
Missing Numbers

Four numbers are missing from the box. When all 15 numbers are together and in order, they increase by 7 and are between 0 and 100. Write the missing numbers.

```
43  71  ?  8
    85     50
29  ?   :  ?
    78     22
99  ?  57
```

The missing numbers are: 15 36 64 92

PAGE 29
Go Figure!

Use the clues to fill in the grid with the correct numbers.

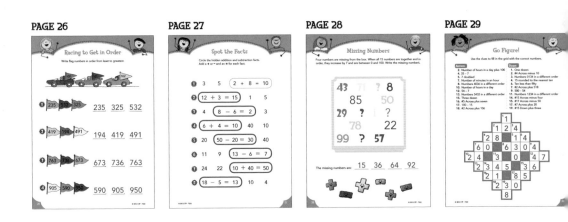

PAGE 30
Mystery Numbers

Read the clues and use the set of numbers to write each mystery number.

1. The number is even. It is greater than 35. It is less than 50.
5 2 6 3 → 36

2. The number is odd. It is greater than 85. It is less than 90.
9 8 2 5 → 89

3. The number is even. It is greater than 60. It is less than 70.
3 7 6 2 → 62

4. The number is odd. It is greater than 45. It is less than 75.
3 9 4 2 → 49

5. The number is even. It is greater than 25. It is less than 30.
2 8 4 3 → 28

6. The number is odd. It is greater than 80. It is less than 95.
1 9 7 4 → 91

PAGE 31
Search for Time and Place

Find and circle the words from the Word Box.

FRONT NEXT BESIDE BEFORE AFTER
BETWEEN FIRST BELOW BACK ABOVE
EARLY LAST MIDDLE PAST LATE

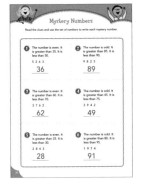

PAGE 32
High in the Sky

Write the missing numbers.

1. 7, 17, 27, 37, 47, 57, 67, 77
2. 30, 28, 26, 24, 22, 20, 18, 16
3. 95, 85, 75, 65, 55, 45, 35, 25
4. 1, 5, 9, 13, 17, 21, 25, 29
5. 10, 21, 32, 43, 54, 65, 76, 87

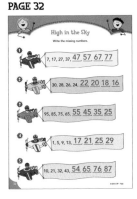

PAGE 33
Math Riddle

Write the differences under the problems. To answer the riddle, find the letters that match the differences and write them on the lines below.

Math Box
14 11 21 17 15 9 10
N E S G V I T H

Why is six afraid of seven? Because...

15 17 16 15 18
−7 −6 −9 −4 −4
8 11 7 11 14

18 15 20 11 20 19
−7 −3 −9 −10 −8 −8
11 15 6 10 9 14 15 14 11

ANSWER
SEVEN EIGHT NINE

PAGE 34
Hidden Sums of 50

Find three numbers in a row across, down, or on a diagonal that add up to the sum of 50. Circle each set of three numbers.

I found 9 sums of 50.

PAGE 35
More Tricky Triangles

Count the total number of triangles you see in each design. Be careful. Some triangles may be hidden!

1. 6 triangles
2. 8 triangles
3. 5 triangles
4. 16 triangles

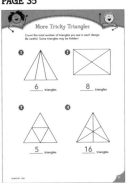

PAGE 36
Fractured Fractions

Draw lines on the shapes below. Then shade them.
Possible answers include:

1. Divide the rectangle into thirds. Then shade ⅓.
2. Divide the circle into half. Then shade ½.
3. Divide the circle into fourths. Then shade ¼.
4. Divide the hexagon into sixths. Then shade ⅙.
5. Divide the rectangle into eighths. Then shade ⅛.
6. Divide the square into fourths. Then shade ¼.

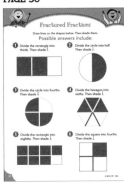

PAGE 37
What Month Is It?

Write the month that answers the question.

1. Mandy's birthday is in June. Kelly's birthday is three months later. In what month is Kelly's birthday?
September

2. Brian's birthday is five months before Jordan's birthday. Jordan's birthday is in August. In what month is Brian's birthday?
March

3. Mrs. Garcia's son turned eight months old in October. In what month was he born?
February

4. Joel visited his uncle for two months. He returned home at the beginning of September. In what month did he arrive at his uncle's house?
July

Months of the Year
January
February
March
April
May
June
July
August
September
October
November
December

PAGE 38

Missing Numbers

Four numbers are missing from the box. When all 13 numbers are together and in order, they increase by 8 and are between 0 and 100. Write the missing numbers.

73		25	
	?	1	9
49		97	
	81	?	
57	?	41	

The missing numbers are: __17__ __33__ __65__ __89__

PAGE 39

Go Figure!

Use the clues to fill in the grid with the correct numbers.

Across
2. 99 + 35
4. 4 + 4 + 4 + 4
5. 25 + 15
7. 90 − 9
9. Numbers 2143 in a different order
10. Number of hours in a day
12. 20 + 5
13. Numbers 6810 in a different order
15. 85 + 6
16. 22 doubled
17. #16 Across plus two
18. #1 Down plus 101

Down
1. 70 − 7
3. Ten times 6 ones
5. Numbers 2346 in a different order
6. One more than 10
8. #14 Down minus one
7. 900 − 59
9. 400 + 20 + 1
11. Numbers 1346 in a different order
14. 100 − 16
15. #15 Across plus five
17. Tens 4 ones
19. #1 Down plus two

PAGE 40

What's My Number?

Circle the correct number.

1. I have three hundreds. I have 2 ones and more than 6 tens.
What number am I?
(372)   352

2. I have seven hundreds. I have 8 tens and more than 7 ones.
What number am I?
(789)   766

3. I have five hundreds. I have 4 tens and less than 5 ones.
What am I?
547   (543)

4. I have nine hundreds. I have less than 7 ones and more than 5 tens.
What am I?
955   (961)

PAGE 41

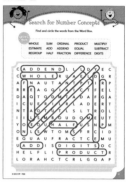

Search for Number Concepts

Find and circle the words from the Word Box.

WHOLE	SUM	ORDINAL	PRODUCT	MULTIPLY
ESTIMATE	ADD	ADDEND	EQUAL	SUBTRACT
REGROUP	HALF	FRACTION	DIFFERENCE	DIGITS

PAGE 42

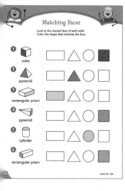

The Shape of Things to Come

Draw shapes in the boxes to continue each pattern.

PAGE 43

Math Riddle

Write the differences under the problems. To answer the riddle, find the letters that match the differences and write them on the lines below.

Match Box

10	8	4	7	6	5	11	12	9
S	O	C	H	A	T	I	M	E

Riddle: What do moths study in school?

18	13	16	18	16	17	12	19
− 6	− 7	− 8	− 9	− 9	− 7	− 8	− 9
12	8	5	7	9	12	6	5	11	4	10

ANSWER **M O T H E M A T I C S**

PAGE 44

Ant's Path to 0

Help the ant find the food. Begin at the number under "Start." Draw the path of numbers that when subtracted equals 0. End at the number above "End."

20	10	5	18	16
9	9	7	3	2
4	6	1	0	6
8	3	4	2	3
5	4	2	1	2

PAGE 45

Groups of the Same

Draw a picture to help you write an equation and solve each problem.

1. 5 pigs in a litter; 2 litters in the pen. Put them together, and you will get _10_
5 . 5 . _10_

2. 3 grapes in a bunch; 3 bunches on the vine. Put them together, and you will get 9
3 . 3 . 3 _9_

3. 2 dogs in a pack; 3 packs fetching sticks. Put them together, and you will get _6_
2 . 2 . 2 _6_

4. 4 horses in a team; 2 teams by the gate. Put them together and you will get _8_
4 . 4 _8_

PAGE 46

Matching Faces

Look at the shaded face of each solid. Color the shape that matches the face.

- cube
- pyramid
- rectangular prism
- pyramid
- cylinder
- rectangular prism

PAGE 47

Do You Recognize My Face?

Write the name of the solid shape that matches each clue.

cube   cone   rectangular prism   sphere   cylinder   pyramid

1. I have faces that are shaped like triangles.
What am I? __pyramid__

2. I have six faces. Each face is a square.
What am I? __cube__

3. I have the same number of sides and corners as a cube.
What am I? __rectangular prism__

4. I have no faces. I only have curved sides.
What am I? __sphere__

5. I have two faces. They are both circles.
What am I? __cylinder__

6. I have only one face. It is a circle.
What am I? __cone__

PAGE 48

Go Figure!

Use the clues to fill in the grid with the correct numbers.

Across
2. #9 down + 200
4. 42 + 34
6. Ten less than twenty-five
7. Number of hours in two days
8. Numbers 1478 in a different order
10. 100 − 16
12. #5 Across plus one
13. Numbers 2468 in a different order
14. #15 Down plus seven
17. 43 doubled
18. 200 + 15

Down
1. #10 Across minus three
3. #4 Across minus 40
5. Numbers 1234 in a different order
8. #17 Across minus eight
9. #7 Across plus 10
11. 400 + 40 + 4
15. 56 doubled
16. Numbers 2358 in a different order
18. #4 Across minus 20
17. 76 + 9
19. 15 + 4

PAGE 49

Missing Numbers

Four numbers are missing from the box. When all 12 numbers are together and in order, they increase by 9 and are between 0 and 101. Write the missing numbers.

10		28	
?	1	?	
37	?	82	
	55		
64	?	100	

The missing numbers are: __19__ __46__ __73__ __91__

Name That Hen!

Read the clues. Then write the correct name below each hen.

Clues

Scratchy laid twice as many eggs as hen C.
Hen A laid three more eggs than Henny-Penny.
One hen is named Edith.
One hen laid 2 eggs, one laid 4 eggs, and one laid 5 eggs.

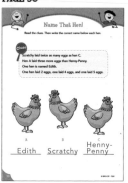

A
Edith

B
Scratchy

C
Henny-Penny

What's the Magic Rule?

Subtract to find the magic rule that changes the IN numbers to the OUT numbers.
Then fill in the missing numbers and write the rule at the bottom of each box.

IN	OUT
18	15
12	9
10	7
16	13
20	17
15	12
RULE: − 3	

IN	OUT
15	10
16	11
17	12
18	13
19	14
10	5
RULE: −5	

IN	OUT
5	1
12	8
8	4
10	6
14	10
20	16
RULE: −4	

IN	OUT
12	6
10	4
16	10
14	8
11	5
18	12
RULE: −6	